Alison Bell's

MORE GRADED PIECES FOR PIANO

BOOK 1 : EASY

ALL MY LOVING, 24
BRIGHT EYES, 31
CABARET, 17
CAN'T BUY ME LOVE, 38
CRUISING DOWN THE RIVER, 6
HE'S GOT THE WHOLE WORLD IN HIS HANDS, 11
IF MY FRIENDS COULD SEE ME NOW, 8
JUST AN OLD FASHIONED GIRL, 34
LA CUCARACHA, 40
LAMBETH WALK, 12
PENNIES FROM HEAVEN, 36
STRANGERS IN THE NIGHT, 28
TALES OF THE UNEXPECTED (Theme), 20
THE SOUND OF SILENCE, 4
UNDER PARIS SKIES (Sous Le Ciel De Paris), 2
WE'LL MEET AGAIN, 26
WHO DO YOU THINK YOU ARE KIDDING MR. HITLER?, 14

Exclusive distributors:
Music Sales Limited, 8/9 Frith Street, London W1V 5TZ. England.
Music Sales Pty Limited, 120 Rothschild Avenue, Rosebery, NSW 2018, Australia.

This book © Copyright 1990: Wise Publications
Order No. AM78809/ISBN 0.7119.2172.5

Art direction by Mike Bell. Book designed by Evelina Frescura
Cover photography by Peter Wood
Typeset by Capital Setters

Music Sales' complete catalogue lists thousands of titles and is free
from your local music shop, or direct from Music Sales Limited. Please send £1 in stamps
for postage to Music Sales Limited, 8/9 Frith Street, London W1V 5TZ.

Printed in the United Kingdom by
J.B. Offset Printers (Marks Tey) Limited, Marks Tey, Essex.

UNDER PARIS SKIES
(SOUS LE CIEL DE PARIS)

ENGLISH WORDS: KIM GANNON
ORIGINAL WORDS: JEAN DREJAC
MUSIC: HUBERT GIRAUD

THE SOUND OF SILENCE

WORDS & MUSIC: PAUL SIMON

CRUISING DOWN THE RIVER

WORDS & MUSIC: EILY BEADELL & NELL TOLLERTON

IF MY FRIENDS COULD SEE ME NOW

WORDS: DOROTHY FIELDS
MUSIC: CY COLEMAN

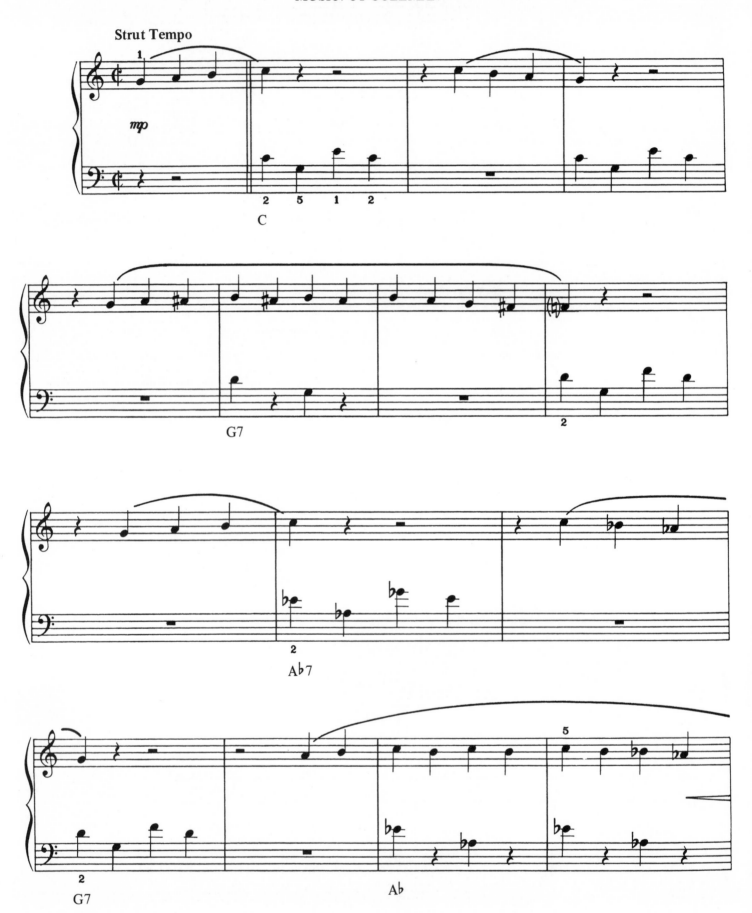

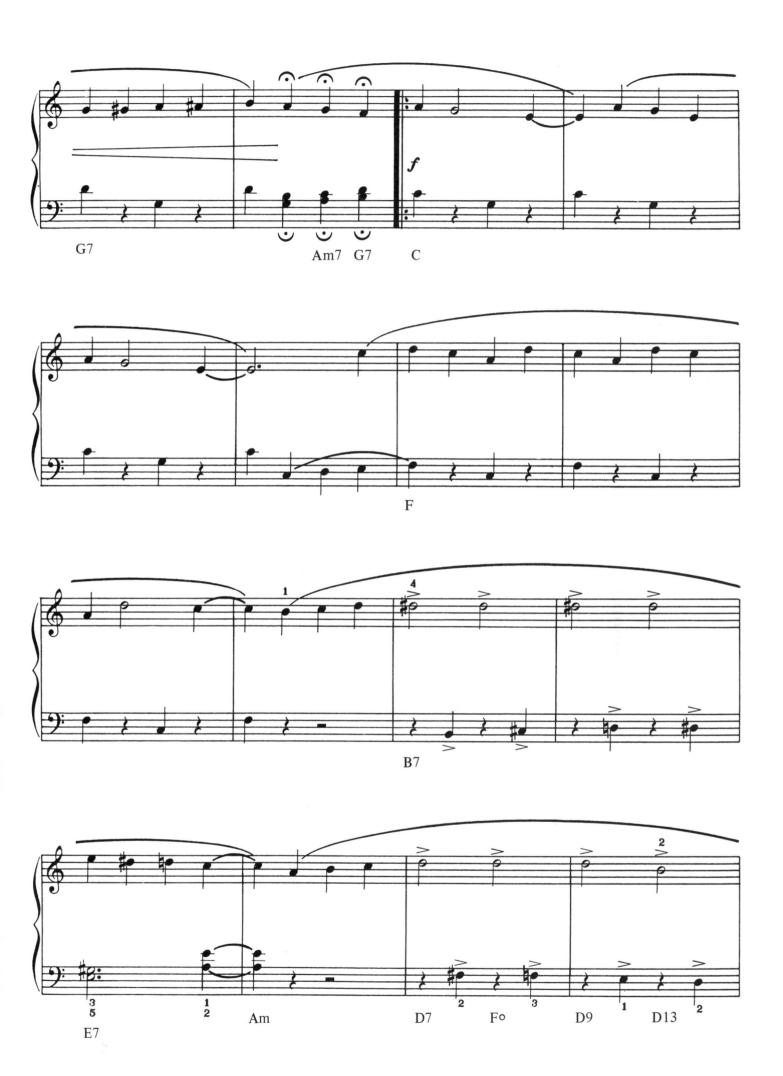

HE'S GOT THE WHOLE WORLD
IN HIS HANDS

TRADITIONAL

LAMBETH WALK

MUSIC: NOEL GAY
WORDS: DOUGLAS FURBER & ARTHUR ROSE

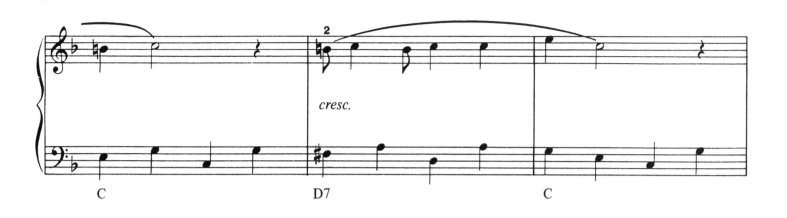

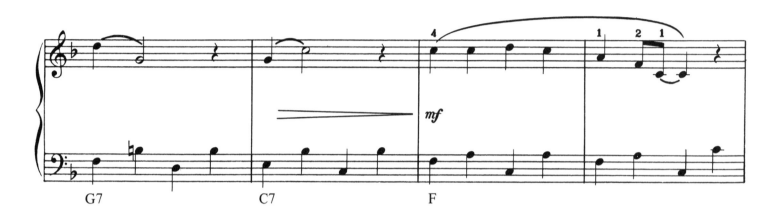

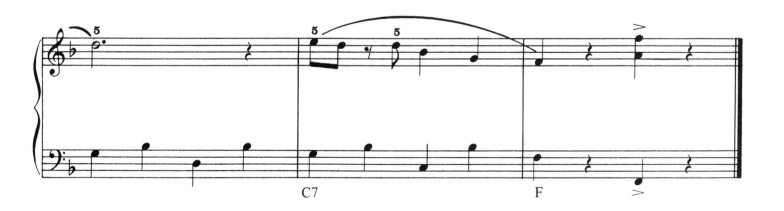

WHO DO YOU THINK YOU ARE KIDDING MR. HITLER?

WORDS: JIMMY PERRY
MUSIC: JIMMY PERRY AND DEREK TAVERNER

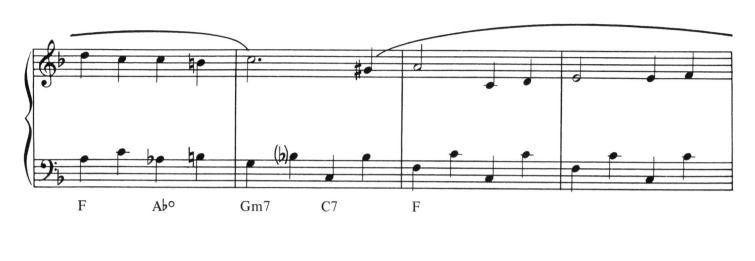

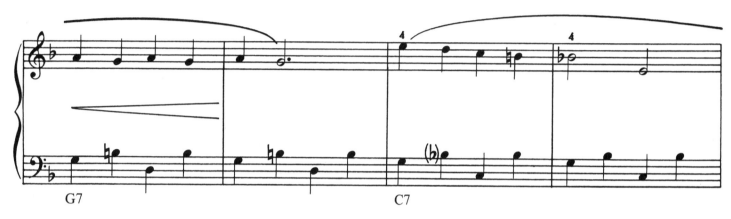

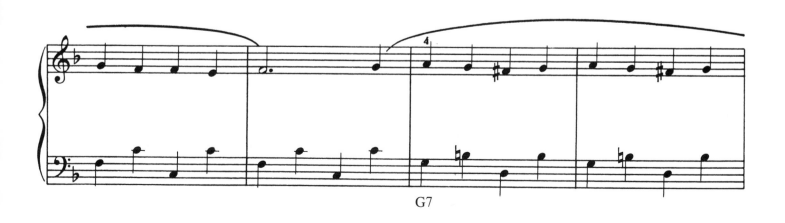

CABARET

MUSIC: JOHN KANDER
LYRICS: FRED EBB

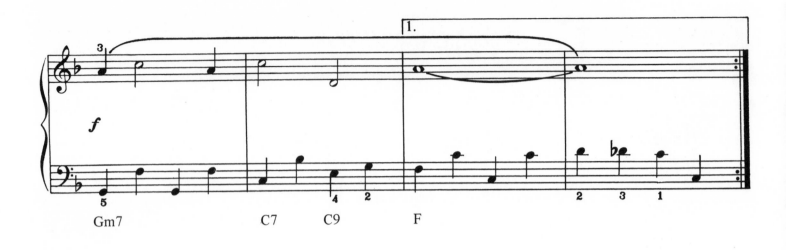

Gm7   C7   C9   F

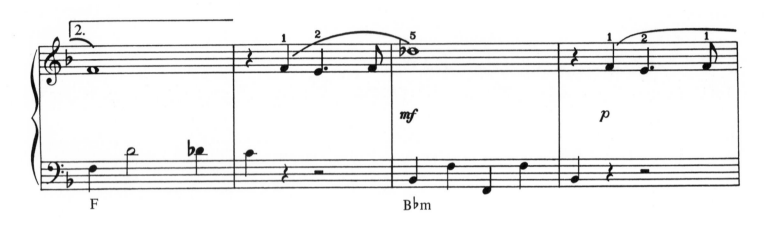

F   B♭m

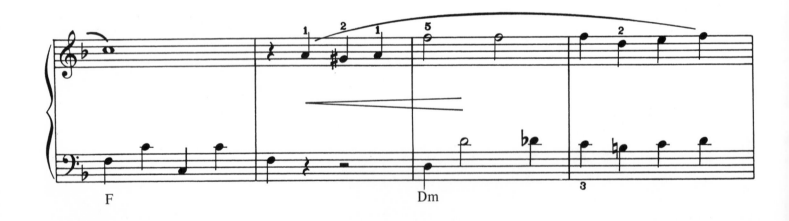

F   Dm

C7   F

TALES OF THE UNEXPECTED
(Theme From)

COMPOSED: RON GRAINER

23

ALL MY LOVING

WORDS & MUSIC: JOHN LENNON & PAUL McCARTNEY

WE'LL MEET AGAIN

WORDS & MUSIC: ROSS PARKER & HUGHIE CHARLES

STRANGERS IN THE NIGHT

WORDS: CHARLES SINGLETON & EDDIE SNYDER
MUSIC: BERT KAEMPFERT

BRIGHT EYES

WORDS & MUSIC: MIKE BATT

JUST AN OLD FASHIONED GIRL

WORDS & MUSIC: MARVE FISHER

PENNIES FROM HEAVEN

WORDS: JOHN BURKE
MUSIC: ARTHUR JOHNSTON

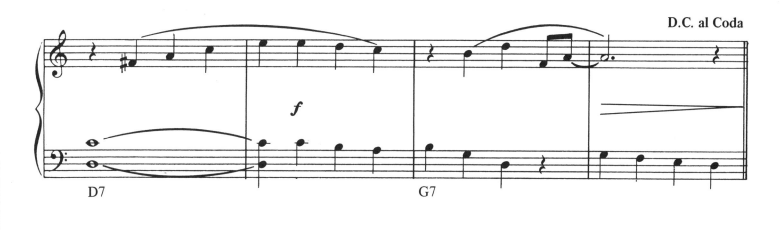

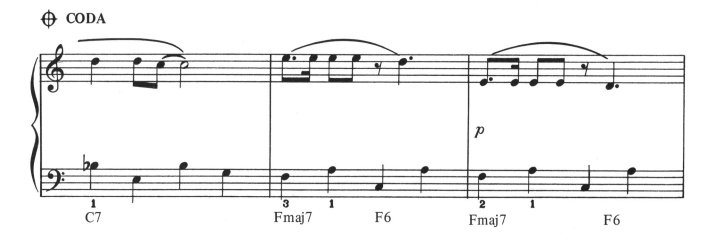

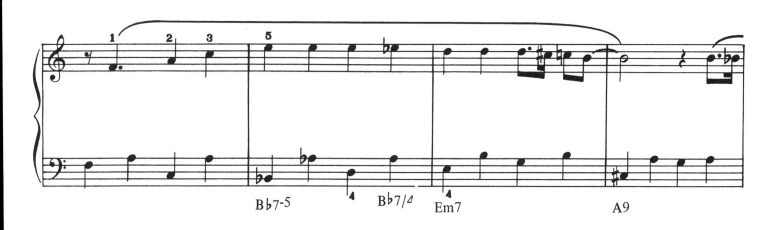

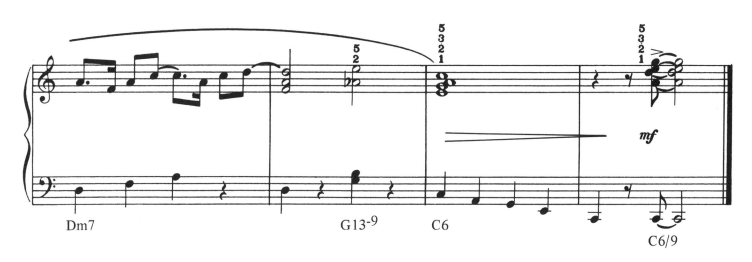

CAN'T BUY ME LOVE

WORDS & MUSIC: JOHN LENNON & PAUL McCARTNEY

LA CUCARACHA

TRADITIONAL